This book belongs to

....

Address

....

....

....

....

Telephone/Fax

....

a

Name ....
Address ....
....
.........................Zip/Postal code........................
Phone ....
Fax ....
Mobile ....
e-mail ....

Name ....
Address ....
....
.........................Zip/Postal code ....
Phone ....
Fax ....
Mobile ....
e-mail ....

Name ....
Address ....
....
.........................Zip/Postal code........................
Phone ....
Fax ....
Mobile ....
e-mail ....

Name ....
Address ....
....
.........................Zip/Postal code........................
Phone ....
Fax ....
Mobile ....
e-mail ....

Name ....
Address ....
....
.........................Zip/Postal code........................
Phone ....
Fax ....
Mobile ....
e-mail ....

Name ....
Address ....
....
.... Zip/Postal code........................
Phone ....
Fax ....
Mobile ....
e-mail ....

Name ....
Address ....
....
.........................Zip/Postal code........................
Phone ....
Fax ....
Mobile ....
e-mail ....

Name ....
Address ....
....
...........................Zip/Postal code......................
Phone ....
Fax ....
Mobile ....
e-mail ....

Name ....
Address ....
....
...........................Zip/Postal code......................
Phone ....
Fax ....
Mobile ....
e-mail ....

Name ....
Address ....
....
...........................Zip/Postal code......................
Phone ....
Fax ....
Mobile ....
e-mail ....

Name ....
Address ....
....
...........................Zip/Postal code......................
Phone ....
Fax ....
Mobile ....
e-mail ....

Name ....
Address ....
....
...........................Zip/Postal code......................
Phone ....
Fax ....
Mobile ....
e-mail ....

Name ....
Address ....
....
...........................Zip/Postal code......................
Phone ....
Fax ....
Mobile ....
e-mail ....

Name ....
Address ....
....
...........................Zip/Postal code......................
Phone ....
Fax ....
Mobile ....
e-mail ....

Name ....
Address ....
....
...........................Zip/Postal code.....................
Phone ....
Fax ....
Mobile ....
e-mail ....

Name ....
Address ....
....
...........................Zip/Postal code ....
Phone ....
Fax ....
Mobile ....
e-mail ....

Name ....
Address ....
....
...........................Zip/Postal code.....................
Phone ....
Fax ....
Mobile ....
e-mail ....

Name ....
Address ....
....
...........................Zip/Postal code.....................
Phone ....
Fax ....
Mobile ....
e-mail ....

Name ....
Address ....
....
...........................Zip/Postal code.....................
Phone ....
Fax ....
Mobile ....
e-mail ....

Name ....
Address ....
....
...........................Zip/Postal code.....................
Phone ....
Fax ....
Mobile ....
e-mail ....

Name ....
Address ....
....
...........................Zip/Postal code.....................
Phone ....
Fax ....
Mobile ....
e-mail ....

Name ....
Address ....
....
........................Zip/Postal code...................
Phone ....
Fax ....
Mobile ....
e-mail ....

Name ....
Address ....
....
........................Zip/Postal code...................
Phone ....
Fax ....
Mobile ....
e-mail ....

Name ....
Address ....
....
........................Zip/Postal code...................
Phone ....
Fax ....
Mobile ....
e-mail ....

Name ....
Address ....
....
........................Zip/Postal code...................
Phone ....
Fax ....
Mobile ....
e-mail ....

Name ....
Address ....
....
........................Zip/Postal code...................
Phone ....
Fax ....
Mobile ....
e-mail ....

Name ....
Address ....
....
........................Zip/Postal code...................
Phone ....
Fax ....
Mobile ....
e-mail ....

Name ....
Address ....
....
........................Zip/Postal code...................
Phone ....
Fax ....
Mobile ....
e-mail ....

Name ....
Address ....
....
.............................Zip/Postal code.....................
Phone ....
Fax ....
Mobile ....
e-mail ....

Name ....
Address ....
....
.............................Zip/Postal code.....................
Phone ....
Fax ....
Mobile ....
e-mail ....

Name ....
Address ....
....
.............................Zip/Postal code.....................
Phone ....
Fax ....
Mobile ....
e-mail ....

Name ....
Address ....
....
.............................Zip/Postal code.....................
Phone ....
Fax ....
Mobile ....
e-mail ....

Name ....
Address ....
....
.............................Zip/Postal code.....................
Phone ....
Fax ....
Mobile ....
e-mail ....

Name ....
Address ....
....
.............................Zip/Postal code.....................
Phone ....
Fax ....
Mobile ....
e-mail ....

Name ....
Address ....
....
.............................Zip/Postal code.....................
Phone ....
Fax ....
Mobile ....
e-mail ....

b

Name ....
Address ....
....
...........................Zip/Postal code....................
Phone ....
Fax ....
Mobile ....
e-mail ....

Name ....
Address ....
....
...........................Zip/Postal code....................
Phone ....
Fax ....
Mobile ....
e-mail ....

Name ....
Address ....
....
...........................Zip/Postal code....................
Phone ....
Fax ....
Mobile ....
e-mail ....

Name ....
Address ....
....
...........................Zip/Postal code....................
Phone ....
Fax ....
Mobile ....
e-mail ....

Name ....
Address ....
....
...........................Zip/Postal code....................
Phone ....
Fax ....
Mobile ....
e-mail ....

Name ....
Address ....
....
...........................Zip/Postal code....................
Phone ....
Fax ....
Mobile ....
e-mail ....

Name ....
Address ....
....
...........................Zip/Postal code....................
Phone ....
Fax ....
Mobile ....
e-mail ....

C

C

Name ....
Address ....
....
........................Zip/Postal code....................
Phone ....
Fax ....
Mobile ....
e-mail ....

Name ....
Address ....
....
........................Zip/Postal code....................
Phone ....
Fax ....
Mobile ....
e-mail ....

Name ....
Address ....
....
........................Zip/Postal code....................
Phone ....
Fax ....
Mobile ....
e-mail ....

Name ....
Address ....
....
........................Zip/Postal code....................
Phone ....
Fax ....
Mobile ....
e-mail ....

Name ....
Address ....
....
........................Zip/Postal code....................
Phone ....
Fax ....
Mobile ....
e-mail ....

Name ....
Address ....
....
........................Zip/Postal code....................
Phone ....
Fax ....
Mobile ....
e-mail ....

Name ....
Address ....
....
........................Zip/Postal code....................
Phone ....
Fax ....
Mobile ....
e-mail ....

Name ....
Address ....
....
....................Zip/Postal code..................
Phone ....
Fax ....
Mobile ....
e-mail ....

Name ....
Address ....
....
....................Zip/Postal code ....
Phone ....
Fax ....
Mobile ....
e-mail ....

Name ....
Address ....
....
....................Zip/Postal code..................
Phone ....
Fax ....
Mobile ....
e-mail ....

Name ....
Address ....
....
....................Zip/Postal code..................
Phone ....
Fax ....
Mobile ....
e-mail ....

Name ....
Address ....
....
....................Zip/Postal code..................
Phone ....
Fax ....
Mobile ....
e-mail ....

Name ....
Address ....
....
....................Zip/Postal code..................
Phone ....
Fax ....
Mobile ....
e-mail ....

Name ....
Address ....
....
....................Zip/Postal code..................
Phone ....
Fax ....
Mobile ....
e-mail ....

Name ....
Address ....
....
.........................Zip/Postal code................
Phone ....
Fax ....
Mobile ....
e-mail ....

Name ....
Address ....
....
.........................Zip/Postal code................
Phone ....
Fax ....
Mobile ....
e-mail ....

Name ....
Address ....
....
.........................Zip/Postal code................
Phone ....
Fax ....
Mobile ....
e-mail ....

Name ....
Address ....
....
.........................Zip/Postal code................
Phone ....
Fax ....
Mobile ....
e-mail ....

Name ....
Address ....
....
.........................Zip/Postal code................
Phone ....
Fax ....
Mobile ....
e-mail ....

Name ....
Address ....
....
.........................Zip/Postal code................
Phone ....
Fax ....
Mobile ....
e-mail ....

Name ....
Address ....
....
.........................Zip/Postal code................
Phone ....
Fax ....
Mobile ....
e-mail ....

d

Name ....
Address ....
....
......................Zip/Postal code....................
Phone ....
Fax ....
Mobile ....
e-mail ....

Name ....
Address ....
....
......................Zip/Postal code ....
Phone ....
Fax ....
Mobile ....
e-mail ....

Name ....
Address ....
....
......................Zip/Postal code....................
Phone ....
Fax ....
Mobile ....
e-mail ....

Name ....
Address ....
....
......................Zip/Postal code....................
Phone ....
Fax ....
Mobile ....
e-mail ....

Name ....
Address ....
....
......................Zip/Postal code....................
Phone ....
Fax ....
Mobile ....
e-mail ....

Name ....
Address ....
....
......................Zip/Postal code....................
Phone ....
Fax ....
Mobile ....
e-mail ....

Name ....
Address ....
....
......................Zip/Postal code....................
Phone ....
Fax ....
Mobile ....
e-mail ....

Name ....
Address ....
....
.......................Zip/Postal code....................
Phone ....
Fax ....
Mobile ....
e-mail ....

Name ....
Address ....
....
.......................Zip/Postal code....................
Phone ....
Fax ....
Mobile ....
e-mail ....

Name ....
Address ....
....
.......................Zip/Postal code....................
Phone ....
Fax ....
Mobile ....
e-mail ....

Name ....
Address ....
....
.......................Zip/Postal code....................
Phone ....
Fax ....
Mobile ....
e-mail ....

Name ....
Address ....
....
.......................Zip/Postal code....................
Phone ....
Fax ....
Mobile ....
e-mail ....

Name ....
Address ....
....
.......................Zip/Postal code....................
Phone ....
Fax ....
Mobile ....
e-mail ....

Name ....
Address ....
....
.......................Zip/Postal code....................
Phone ....
Fax ....
Mobile ....
e-mail ....

d

Name ....
Address ....
....
.............................Zip/Postal code.....................
Phone ....
Fax ....
Mobile ....
e-mail ....

Name ....
Address ....
....
.............................Zip/Postal code ....
Phone ....
Fax ....
Mobile ....
e-mail ....

Name ....
Address ....
....
.............................Zip/Postal code.....................
Phone ....
Fax ....
Mobile ....
e-mail ....

Name ....
Address ....
....
.............................Zip/Postal code.....................
Phone ....
Fax ....
Mobile ....
e-mail ....

Name ....
Address ....
....
.............................Zip/Postal code.....................
Phone ....
Fax ....
Mobile ....
e-mail ....

Name ....
Address ....
....
.............................Zip/Postal code.....................
Phone ....
Fax ....
Mobile ....
e-mail ....

Name ....
Address ....
....
.............................Zip/Postal code.....................
Phone ....
Fax ....
Mobile ....
e-mail ....

Name ....
Address ....
....
..........................Zip/Postal code.......................
Phone ....
Fax ....
Mobile ....
e-mail ....

Name ....
Address ....
....
..........................Zip/Postal code.......................
Phone ....
Fax ....
Mobile ....
e-mail ....

Name ....
Address ....
....
..........................Zip/Postal code.......................
Phone ....
Fax ....
Mobile ....
e-mail ....

Name ....
Address ....
....
..........................Zip/Postal code.......................
Phone ....
Fax ....
Mobile ....
e-mail ....

Name ....
Address ....
....
..........................Zip/Postal code.......................
Phone ....
Fax ....
Mobile ....
e-mail ....

Name ....
Address ....
....
..........................Zip/Postal code.......................
Phone ....
Fax ....
Mobile ....
e-mail ....

Name ....
Address ....
....
..........................Zip/Postal code.......................
Phone ....
Fax ....
Mobile ....
e-mail ....

Name ....
Address ....
....
........................Zip/Postal code....................
Phone ....
Fax ....
Mobile ....
e-mail ....

Name ....
Address ....
....
........................Zip/Postal code....................
Phone ....
Fax ....
Mobile ....
e-mail ....

Name ....
Address ....
....
........................Zip/Postal code....................
Phone ....
Fax ....
Mobile ....
e-mail ....

Name ....
Address ....
....
........................Zip/Postal code....................
Phone ....
Fax ....
Mobile ....
e-mail ....

Name ....
Address ....
....
........................Zip/Postal code....................
Phone ....
Fax ....
Mobile ....
e-mail ....

Name ....
Address ....
....
........................Zip/Postal code....................
Phone ....
Fax ....
Mobile ....
e-mail ....

Name ....
Address ....
....
........................Zip/Postal code....................
Phone ....
Fax ....
Mobile ....
e-mail ....

Name ....
Address ....
....
.........................Zip/Postal code...................
Phone ....
Fax ....
Mobile ....
e-mail ....

Name ....
Address ....
....
.........................Zip/Postal code...................
Phone ....
Fax ....
Mobile ....
e-mail ....

Name ....
Address ....
....
.........................Zip/Postal code...................
Phone ....
Fax ....
Mobile ....
e-mail ....

Name ....
Address ....
....
.........................Zip/Postal code...................
Phone ....
Fax ....
Mobile ....
e-mail ....

Name ....
Address ....
....
.........................Zip/Postal code...................
Phone ....
Fax ....
Mobile ....
e-mail ....

Name ....
Address ....
....
.........................Zip/Postal code...................
Phone ....
Fax ....
Mobile ....
e-mail ....

Name ....
Address ....
....
.........................Zip/Postal code...................
Phone ....
Fax ....
Mobile ....
e-mail ....

Name ....
Address ....
....
.........................Zip/Postal code.....................
Phone ....
Fax ....
Mobile ....
e-mail ....

Name ....
Address ....
....
.........................Zip/Postal code.....................
Phone ....
Fax ....
Mobile ....
e-mail ....

Name ....
Address ....
....
.........................Zip/Postal code.....................
Phone ....
Fax ....
Mobile ....
e-mail ....

Name ....
Address ....
....
.........................Zip/Postal code.....................
Phone ....
Fax ....
Mobile ....
e-mail ....

Name ....
Address ....
....
.........................Zip/Postal code.....................
Phone ....
Fax ....
Mobile ....
e-mail ....

Name ....
Address ....
....
.........................Zip/Postal code.....................
Phone ....
Fax ....
Mobile ....
e-mail ....

Name ....
Address ....
....
.........................Zip/Postal code.....................
Phone ....
Fax ....
Mobile ....
e-mail ....

Name ....
Address ....
....
........................Zip/Postal code....................
Phone ....
Fax ....
Mobile ....
e-mail ....

Name ....
Address ....
....
........................Zip/Postal code....................
Phone ....
Fax ....
Mobile ....
e-mail ....

Name ....
Address ....
....
........................Zip/Postal code....................
Phone ....
Fax ....
Mobile ....
e-mail ....

Name ....
Address ....
....
........................Zip/Postal code....................
Phone ....
Fax ....
Mobile ....
e-mail ....

Name ....
Address ....
....
........................Zip/Postal code....................
Phone ....
Fax ....
Mobile ....
e-mail ....

Name ....
Address ....
....
........................Zip/Postal code....................
Phone ....
Fax ....
Mobile ....
e-mail ....

Name ....
Address ....
....
........................Zip/Postal code....................
Phone ....
Fax ....
Mobile ....
e-mail ....

Name ....
Address ....
....
.........................Zip/Postal code.............
Phone ....
Fax ....
Mobile ....
e-mail ....

Name ....
Address ....
....
.........................Zip/Postal code.............
Phone ....
Fax ....
Mobile ....
e-mail ....

Name ....
Address ....
....
.........................Zip/Postal code.............
Phone ....
Fax ....
Mobile ....
e-mail ....

Name ....
Address ....
....
.........................Zip/Postal code.............
Phone ....
Fax ....
Mobile ....
e-mail ....

Name ....
Address ....
....
.........................Zip/Postal code.............
Phone ....
Fax ....
Mobile ....
e-mail ....

Name ....
Address ....
....
.........................Zip/Postal code.............
Phone ....
Fax ....
Mobile ....
e-mail ....

Name ....
Address ....
....
.........................Zip/Postal code.............
Phone ....
Fax ....
Mobile ....
e-mail ....

f

Name ....
Address ....
....
.........................Zip/Postal code.....................
Phone ....
Fax ....
Mobile ....
e-mail ....

Name ....
Address ....
....
.........................Zip/Postal code ....
Phone ....
Fax ....
Mobile ....
e-mail ....

Name ....
Address ....
....
.........................Zip/Postal code.....................
Phone ....
Fax ....
Mobile ....
e-mail ....

Name ....
Address ....
....
.........................Zip/Postal code.....................
Phone ....
Fax ....
Mobile ....
e-mail ....

Name ....
Address ....
....
.........................Zip/Postal code.....................
Phone ....
Fax ....
Mobile ....
e-mail ....

Name ....
Address ....
....
.........................Zip/Postal code.....................
Phone ....
Fax ....
Mobile ....
e-mail ....

Name ....
Address ....
....
.........................Zip/Postal code.....................
Phone ....
Fax ....
Mobile ....
e-mail ....

Name ....
Address ....
....
........................Zip/Postal code....................
Phone ....
Fax ....
Mobile ....
e-mail ....

Name ....
Address ....
....
........................Zip/Postal code....................
Phone ....
Fax ....
Mobile ....
e-mail ....

Name ....
Address ....
....
........................Zip/Postal code....................
Phone ....
Fax ....
Mobile ....
e-mail ....

Name ....
Address ....
....
........................Zip/Postal code....................
Phone ....
Fax ....
Mobile ....
e-mail ....

Name ....
Address ....
....
........................Zip/Postal code....................
Phone ....
Fax ....
Mobile ....
e-mail ....

Name ....
Address ....
....
........................Zip/Postal code....................
Phone ....
Fax ....
Mobile ....
e-mail ....

Name ....
Address ....
....
........................Zip/Postal code.................
Phone ....
Fax ....
Mobile ....
e-mail ....

Name ....
Address ....
....
........................Zip/Postal code.................
Phone ....
Fax ....
Mobile ....
e-mail ....

Name ....
Address ....
....
........................Zip/Postal code.................
Phone ....
Fax ....
Mobile ....
e-mail ....

Name ....
Address ....
....
........................Zip/Postal code.................
Phone ....
Fax ....
Mobile ....
e-mail ....

Name ....
Address ....
....
........................Zip/Postal code.................
Phone ....
Fax ....
Mobile ....
e-mail ....

Name ....
Address ....
....
........................Zip/Postal code.................
Phone ....
Fax ....
Mobile ....
e-mail ....

Name ....
Address ....
....
........................Zip/Postal code.................
Phone ....
Fax ....
Mobile ....
e-mail ....

h

Name ....
Address ....
....
........................Zip/Postal code.................
Phone ....
Fax ....
Mobile ....
e-mail ....

Name ....
Address ....
....
........................Zip/Postal code.................
Phone ....
Fax ....
Mobile ....
e-mail ....

Name ....
Address ....
....
........................Zip/Postal code.................
Phone ....
Fax ....
Mobile ....
e-mail ....

Name ....
Address ....
....
........................Zip/Postal code.................
Phone ....
Fax ....
Mobile ....
e-mail ....

Name ....
Address ....
....
........................Zip/Postal code.................
Phone ....
Fax ....
Mobile ....
e-mail ....

Name ....
Address ....
....
........................Zip/Postal code.................
Phone ....
Fax ....
Mobile ....
e-mail ....

Name ....
Address ....
....
........................Zip/Postal code.................
Phone ....
Fax ....
Mobile ....
e-mail ....

h

h

Name ....
Address ....
....
...........................Zip/Postal code....................
Phone ....
Fax ....
Mobile ....
e-mail ....

Name ....
Address ....
....
...........................Zip/Postal code....................
Phone ....
Fax ....
Mobile ....
e-mail ....

Name ....
Address ....
....
...........................Zip/Postal code....................
Phone ....
Fax ....
Mobile ....
e-mail ....

Name ....
Address ....
....
...........................Zip/Postal code....................
Phone ....
Fax ....
Mobile ....
e-mail ....

Name ....
Address ....
....
...........................Zip/Postal code....................
Phone ....
Fax ....
Mobile ....
e-mail ....

Name ....
Address ....
....
...........................Zip/Postal code....................
Phone ....
Fax ....
Mobile ....
e-mail ....

Name ....
Address ....
....
.........................Zip/Postal code....................
Phone ....
Fax ....
Mobile ....
e-mail ....

Name ....
Address ....
....
.........................Zip/Postal code ....
Phone ....
Fax ....
Mobile ....
e-mail ....

Name ....
Address ....
....
.........................Zip/Postal code....................
Phone ....
Fax ....
Mobile ....
e-mail ....

Name ....
Address ....
....
.........................Zip/Postal code....................
Phone ....
Fax ....
Mobile ....
e-mail ....

Name ....
Address ....
....
.........................Zip/Postal code....................
Phone ....
Fax ....
Mobile ....
e-mail ....

Name ....
Address ....
....
.........................Zip/Postal code....................
Phone ....
Fax ....
Mobile ....
e-mail ....

Name ....
Address ....
....
.........................Zip/Postal code....................
Phone ....
Fax ....
Mobile ....
e-mail ....

Name ....
Address ....
....
........................Zip/Postal code.....................
Phone ....
Fax ....
Mobile ....
e-mail ....

Name ....
Address ....
....
........................Zip/Postal code ....
Phone ....
Fax ....
Mobile ....
e-mail ....

Name ....
Address ....
....
........................Zip/Postal code.....................
Phone ....
Fax ....
Mobile ....
e-mail ....

Name ....
Address ....
....
........................Zip/Postal code.....................
Phone ....
Fax ....
Mobile ....
e-mail ....

Name ....
Address ....
....
........................Zip/Postal code.....................
Phone ....
Fax ....
Mobile ....
e-mail ....

Name ....
Address ....
....
........................Zip/Postal code.....................
Phone ....
Fax ....
Mobile ....
e-mail ....

Name ....
Address ....
....
........................Zip/Postal code.....................
Phone ....
Fax ....
Mobile ....
e-mail ....

Name ....
Address ....
....
.........................Zip/Postal code....................
Phone ....
Fax ....
Mobile ....
e-mail ....

Name ....
Address ....
....
.........................Zip/Postal code....................
Phone ....
Fax ....
Mobile ....
e-mail ....

Name ....
Address ....
....
.........................Zip/Postal code....................
Phone ....
Fax ....
Mobile ....
e-mail ....

Name ....
Address ....
....
.........................Zip/Postal code....................
Phone ....
Fax ....
Mobile ....
e-mail ....

Name ....
Address ....
....
.........................Zip/Postal code....................
Phone ....
Fax ....
Mobile ....
e-mail ....

Name ....
Address ....
....
.........................Zip/Postal code....................
Phone ....
Fax ....
Mobile ....
e-mail ....

Name ....
Address ....
....
.........................Zip/Postal code....................
Phone ....
Fax ....
Mobile ....
e-mail ....

Name ....
Address ....
....
.........................Zip/Postal code....................
Phone ....
Fax ....
Mobile ....
e-mail ....

Name ....
Address ....
....
.........................Zip/Postal code....................
Phone ....
Fax ....
Mobile ....
e-mail ....

Name ....
Address ....
....
.........................Zip/Postal code....................
Phone ....
Fax ....
Mobile ....
e-mail ....

Name ....
Address ....
....
.........................Zip/Postal code....................
Phone ....
Fax ....
Mobile ....
e-mail ....

Name ....
Address ....
....
.........................Zip/Postal code....................
Phone ....
Fax ....
Mobile ....
e-mail ....

Name ....
Address ....
....
.........................Zip/Postal code....................
Phone ....
Fax ....
Mobile ....
e-mail ....

Name ....
Address ....
....
.........................Zip/Postal code....................
Phone ....
Fax ....
Mobile ....
e-mail ....

Name ....
Address ....
....
.........................Zip/Postal code.....................
Phone ....
Fax ....
Mobile ....
e-mail ....

Name ....
Address ....
....
.........................Zip/Postal code.....................
Phone ....
Fax ....
Mobile ....
e-mail ....

Name ....
Address ....
....
.........................Zip/Postal code.....................
Phone ....
Fax ....
Mobile ....
e-mail ....

Name ....
Address ....
....
.........................Zip/Postal code.....................
Phone ....
Fax ....
Mobile ....
e-mail ....

Name ....
Address ....
....
.........................Zip/Postal code.....................
Phone ....
Fax ....
Mobile ....
e-mail ....

Name ....
Address ....
....
.........................Zip/Postal code.....................
Phone ....
Fax ....
Mobile ....
e-mail ....

Name ....
Address ....
....
.........................Zip/Postal code.....................
Phone ....
Fax ....
Mobile ....
e-mail ....

Name ....
Address ....
....
..................Zip/Postal code..................
Phone ....
Fax ....
Mobile ....
e-mail ....

Name ....
Address ....
....
..................Zip/Postal code..................
Phone ....
Fax ....
Mobile ....
e-mail ....

Name ....
Address ....
....
..................Zip/Postal code..................
Phone ....
Fax ....
Mobile ....
e-mail ....

Name ....
Address ....
....
..................Zip/Postal code..................
Phone ....
Fax ....
Mobile ....
e-mail ....

Name ....
Address ....
....
..................Zip/Postal code..................
Phone ....
Fax ....
Mobile ....
e-mail ....

Name ....
Address ....
....
..................Zip/Postal code..................
Phone ....
Fax ....
Mobile ....
e-mail ....

Name ....
Address ....
....
..................Zip/Postal code..................
Phone ....
Fax ....
Mobile ....
e-mail ....

Name ....
Address ....
....
.........................Zip/Postal code.....................
Phone ....
Fax ....
Mobile ....
e-mail ....

Name ....
Address ....
....
.........................Zip/Postal code.....................
Phone ....
Fax ....
Mobile ....
e-mail ....

Name ....
Address ....
....
.........................Zip/Postal code.....................
Phone ....
Fax ....
Mobile ....
e-mail ....

Name ....
Address ....
....
.........................Zip/Postal code.....................
Phone ....
Fax ....
Mobile ....
e-mail ....

Name ....
Address ....
....
.........................Zip/Postal code.....................
Phone ....
Fax ....
Mobile ....
e-mail ....

Name ....
Address ....
....
.........................Zip/Postal code.....................
Phone ....
Fax ....
Mobile ....
e-mail ....

Name ....
Address ....
....
.........................Zip/Postal code.....................
Phone ....
Fax ....
Mobile ....
e-mail ....

k

Name ....
Address ....
....
........................Zip/Postal code...................
Phone ....
Fax ....
Mobile ....
e-mail ....

Name ....
Address ....
....
........................Zip/Postal code...................
Phone ....
Fax ....
Mobile ....
e-mail ....

Name ....
Address ....
....
........................Zip/Postal code...................
Phone ....
Fax ....
Mobile ....
e-mail ....

Name ....
Address ....
....
........................Zip/Postal code...................
Phone ....
Fax ....
Mobile ....
e-mail ....

Name ....
Address ....
....
........................Zip/Postal code...................
Phone ....
Fax ....
Mobile ....
e-mail ....

Name ....
Address ....
....
........................Zip/Postal code...................
Phone ....
Fax ....
Mobile ....
e-mail ....

Name ....
Address ....
....
........................Zip/Postal code...................
Phone ....
Fax ....
Mobile ....
e-mail ....

Name ....
Address ....
....
.........................Zip/Postal code.......................
Phone ....
Fax ....
Mobile ....
e-mail ....

Name ....
Address ....
....
.........................Zip/Postal code....................
Phone ....
Fax ....
Mobile ....
e-mail ....

Name ....
Address ....
....
.........................Zip/Postal code.......................
Phone ....
Fax ....
Mobile ....
e-mail ....

Name ....
Address ....
....
.........................Zip/Postal code.......................
Phone ....
Fax ....
Mobile ....
e-mail ....

Name ....
Address ....
....
.........................Zip/Postal code.......................
Phone ....
Fax ....
Mobile ....
e-mail ....

Name ....
Address ....
....
.........................Zip/Postal code.......................
Phone ....
Fax ....
Mobile ....
e-mail ....

Name ....
Address ....
....
.........................Zip/Postal code.......................
Phone ....
Fax ....
Mobile ....
e-mail ....

Name ....
Address ....
....
...................Zip/Postal code...................
Phone ....
Fax ....
Mobile ....
e-mail ....

Name ....
Address ....
....
...................Zip/Postal code...................
Phone ....
Fax ....
Mobile ....
e-mail ....

Name ....
Address ....
....
...................Zip/Postal code...................
Phone ....
Fax ....
Mobile ....
e-mail ....

Name ....
Address ....
....
...................Zip/Postal code...................
Phone ....
Fax ....
Mobile ....
e-mail ....

Name ....
Address ....
....
...................Zip/Postal code...................
Phone ....
Fax ....
Mobile ....
e-mail ....

Name ....
Address ....
....
...................Zip/Postal code...................
Phone ....
Fax ....
Mobile ....
e-mail ....

Name ....
Address ....
....
...................Zip/Postal code...................
Phone ....
Fax ....
Mobile ....
e-mail ....

1

Name ....
Address ....
....
......................Zip/Postal code...................
Phone ....
Fax ....
Mobile ....
e–mail ....

Name ....
Address ....
....
......................Zip/Postal code...................
Phone ....
Fax ....
Mobile ....
e–mail ....

Name ....
Address ....
....
......................Zip/Postal code...................
Phone ....
Fax ....
Mobile ....
e–mail ....

Name ....
Address ....
....
......................Zip/Postal code...................
Phone ....
Fax ....
Mobile ....
e–mail ....

Name ....
Address ....
....
......................Zip/Postal code...................
Phone ....
Fax ....
Mobile ....
e–mail ....

Name ....
Address ....
....
......................Zip/Postal code...................
Phone ....
Fax ....
Mobile ....
e–mail ....

Name ....
Address ....
....
......................Zip/Postal code...................
Phone ....
Fax ....
Mobile ....
e–mail ....

Name ....
Address ....
....
........................Zip/Postal code.....................
Phone ....
Fax ....
Mobile ....
e-mail ....

Name ....
Address ....
....
........................Zip/Postal code.....................
Phone ....
Fax ....
Mobile ....
e-mail ....

Name ....
Address ....
....
........................Zip/Postal code.....................
Phone ....
Fax ....
Mobile ....
e-mail ....

Name ....
Address ....
....
........................Zip/Postal code.....................
Phone ....
Fax ....
Mobile ....
e-mail ....

Name ....
Address ....
....
........................Zip/Postal code.....................
Phone ....
Fax ....
Mobile ....
e-mail ....

Name ....
Address ....
....
........................Zip/Postal code.....................
Phone ....
Fax ....
Mobile ....
e-mail ....

Name ....
Address ....
....
........................Zip/Postal code.....................
Phone ....
Fax ....
Mobile ....
e-mail ....

Name ....
Address ....
....
.........................Zip/Postal code....................
Phone ....
Fax ....
Mobile ....
e-mail ....

Name ....
Address ....
....
.........................Zip/Postal code....................
Phone ....
Fax ....
Mobile ....
e-mail ....

Name ....
Address ....
....
.........................Zip/Postal code....................
Phone ....
Fax ....
Mobile ....
e-mail ....

Name ....
Address ....
....
.........................Zip/Postal code....................
Phone ....
Fax ....
Mobile ....
e-mail ....

Name ....
Address ....
....
.........................Zip/Postal code....................
Phone ....
Fax ....
Mobile ....
e-mail ....

Name ....
Address ....
....
.........................Zip/Postal code....................
Phone ....
Fax ....
Mobile ....
e-mail ....

Name ....
Address ....
....
.........................Zip/Postal code....................
Phone ....
Fax ....
Mobile ....
e-mail ....

Name ....
Address ....
....
...........................Zip/Postal code.....................
Phone ....
Fax ....
Mobile ....
e-mail ....

Name ....
Address ....
....
...........................Zip/Postal code.....................
Phone ....
Fax ....
Mobile ....
e-mail ....

Name ....
Address ....
....
...........................Zip/Postal code.....................
Phone ....
Fax ....
Mobile ....
e-mail ....

Name ....
Address ....
....
...........................Zip/Postal code.....................
Phone ....
Fax ....
Mobile ....
e-mail ....

Name ....
Address ....
....
...........................Zip/Postal code.....................
Phone ....
Fax ....
Mobile ....
e-mail ....

Name ....
Address ....
....
...........................Zip/Postal code.....................
Phone ....
Fax ....
Mobile ....
e-mail ....

Name ....
Address ....
....
...........................Zip/Postal code.....................
Phone ....
Fax ....
Mobile ....
e-mail ....

Name ....
Address ....
....
.......................Zip/Postal code.....................
Phone ....
Fax ....
Mobile ....
e-mail ....

Name ....
Address ....
....
.......................Zip/Postal code ....
Phone ....
Fax ....
Mobile ....
e-mail ....

Name ....
Address ....
....
.......................Zip/Postal code.....................
Phone ....
Fax ....
Mobile ....
e-mail ....

Name ....
Address ....
....
.......................Zip/Postal code.....................
Phone ....
Fax ....
Mobile ....
e-mail ....

Name ....
Address ....
....
.......................Zip/Postal code.....................
Phone ....
Fax ....
Mobile ....
e-mail ....

Name ....
Address ....
....
.......................Zip/Postal code.....................
Phone ....
Fax ....
Mobile ....
e-mail ....

Name ....
Address ....
....
.......................Zip/Postal code.....................
Phone ....
Fax ....
Mobile ....
e-mail ....

Name ....

Address ....

....

.......................Zip/Postal code.................

Phone ....

Fax ....

Mobile ....

e-mail ....

Name ....

Address ....

....

.......................Zip/Postal code.................

Phone ....

Fax ....

Mobile ....

e-mail ....

Name ....

Address ....

....

.......................Zip/Postal code.................

Phone ....

Fax ....

Mobile ....

e-mail ....

Name ....

Address ....

....

.......................Zip/Postal code.................

Phone ....

Fax ....

Mobile ....

e-mail ....

Name ....

Address ....

....

.......................Zip/Postal code.................

Phone ....

Fax ....

Mobile ....

e-mail ....

Name ....

Address ....

....

.......................Zip/Postal code.................

Phone ....

Fax ....

Mobile ....

e-mail ....

Name ....

Address ....

....

.......................Zip/Postal code.................

Phone ....

Fax ....

Mobile ....

e-mail ....

n

Name ....
Address ....
....
........................Zip/Postal code........................
Phone ....
Fax ....
Mobile ....
e-mail ....

Name ....
Address ....
....
........................Zip/Postal code........................
Phone ....
Fax ....
Mobile ....
e-mail ....

Name ....
Address ....
....
........................Zip/Postal code........................
Phone ....
Fax ....
Mobile ....
e-mail ....

Name ....
Address ....
....
........................Zip/Postal code........................
Phone ....
Fax ....
Mobile ....
e-mail ....

Name ....
Address ....
....
........................Zip/Postal code........................
Phone ....
Fax ....
Mobile ....
e-mail ....

Name ....
Address ....
....
........................Zip/Postal code........................
Phone ....
Fax ....
Mobile ....
e-mail ....

Name ....
Address ....
....
........................Zip/Postal code........................
Phone ....
Fax ....
Mobile ....
e-mail ....

n

Name ....
Address ....
....
........................Zip/Postal code..................
Phone ....
Fax ....
Mobile ....
e-mail ....

Name ....
Address ....
....
........................Zip/Postal code..................
Phone ....
Fax ....
Mobile ....
e-mail ....

Name ....
Address ....
....
........................Zip/Postal code..................
Phone ....
Fax ....
Mobile ....
e-mail ....

Name ....
Address ....
....
........................Zip/Postal code..................
Phone ....
Fax ....
Mobile ....
e-mail ....

Name ....
Address ....
....
........................Zip/Postal code..................
Phone ....
Fax ....
Mobile ....
e-mail ....

Name ....
Address ....
....
........................Zip/Postal code..................
Phone ....
Fax ....
Mobile ....
e-mail ....

Name ....
Address ....
....
........................Zip/Postal code..................
Phone ....
Fax ....
Mobile ....
e-mail ....

Name ....
Address ....
....
......................Zip/Postal code......................
Phone ....
Fax ....
Mobile ....
e-mail ....

Name ....
Address ....
....
......................Zip/Postal code......................
Phone ....
Fax ....
Mobile ....
e-mail ....

Name ....
Address ....
....
......................Zip/Postal code......................
Phone ....
Fax ....
Mobile ....
e-mail ....

Name ....
Address ....
....
......................Zip/Postal code......................
Phone ....
Fax ....
Mobile ....
e-mail ....

Name ....
Address ....
....
......................Zip/Postal code......................
Phone ....
Fax ....
Mobile ....
e-mail ....

Name ....
Address ....
....
......................Zip/Postal code......................
Phone ....
Fax ....
Mobile ....
e-mail ....

Name ....
Address ....
....
......................Zip/Postal code......................
Phone ....
Fax ....
Mobile ....
e-mail ....

Name ....
Address ....
....
.................Zip/Postal code..................
Phone ....
Fax ....
Mobile ....
e-mail ....

Name ....
Address ....
....
.................Zip/Postal code..................
Phone ....
Fax ....
Mobile ....
e-mail ....

Name ....
Address ....
....
.................Zip/Postal code..................
Phone ....
Fax ....
Mobile ....
e-mail ....

Name ....
Address ....
....
.................Zip/Postal code..................
Phone ....
Fax ....
Mobile ....
e-mail ....

Name ....
Address ....
....
.................Zip/Postal code..................
Phone ....
Fax ....
Mobile ....
e-mail ....

Name ....
Address ....
....
.................Zip/Postal code..................
Phone ....
Fax ....
Mobile ....
e-mail ....

Name ....
Address ....
....
.................Zip/Postal code..................
Phone ....
Fax ....
Mobile ....
e-mail ....

Name ....
Address ....
....
.........................Zip/Postal code.....................
Phone ....
Fax ....
Mobile ....
e-mail ....

Name ....
Address ....
....
.........................Zip/Postal code.....................
Phone ....
Fax ....
Mobile ....
e-mail ....

Name ....
Address ....
....
.........................Zip/Postal code.....................
Phone ....
Fax ....
Mobile ....
e-mail ....

Name ....
Address ....
....
.........................Zip/Postal code.....................
Phone ....
Fax ....
Mobile ....
e-mail ....

Name ....
Address ....
....
.........................Zip/Postal code.....................
Phone ....
Fax ....
Mobile ....
e-mail ....

Name ....
Address ....
....
.........................Zip/Postal code.....................
Phone ....
Fax ....
Mobile ....
e-mail ....

Name ....
Address ....
....
.........................Zip/Postal code.....................
Phone ....
Fax ....
Mobile ....
e-mail ....

Name ....
Address ....
....
...........................Zip/Postal code.................
Phone ....
Fax ....
Mobile ....
e-mail ....

Name ....
Address ....
....
...........................Zip/Postal code ....
Phone ....
Fax ....
Mobile ....
e-mail ....

Name ....
Address ....
....
...........................Zip/Postal code.................
Phone ....
Fax ....
Mobile ....
e-mail ....

Name ....
Address ....
....
...........................Zip/Postal code.................
Phone ....
Fax ....
Mobile ....
e-mail ....

Name ....
Address ....
....
...........................Zip/Postal code.................
Phone ....
Fax ....
Mobile ....
e-mail ....

Name ....
Address ....
....
...........................Zip/Postal code.................
Phone ....
Fax ....
Mobile ....
e-mail ....

Name ....
Address ....
....
...........................Zip/Postal code.................
Phone ....
Fax ....
Mobile ....
e-mail ....

Name ....
Address ....
....
.....................Zip/Postal code...................
Phone ....
Fax ....
Mobile ....
e-mail ....

Name ....
Address ....
....
.....................Zip/Postal code...................
Phone ....
Fax ....
Mobile ....
e-mail ....

Name ....
Address ....
....
.....................Zip/Postal code...................
Phone ....
Fax ....
Mobile ....
e-mail ....

Name ....
Address ....
....
.....................Zip/Postal code...................
Phone ....
Fax ....
Mobile ....
e-mail ....

Name ....
Address ....
....
.....................Zip/Postal code...................
Phone ....
Fax ....
Mobile ....
e-mail ....

Name ....
Address ....
....
.....................Zip/Postal code...................
Phone ....
Fax ....
Mobile ....
e-mail ....

Name ....
Address ....
....
.....................Zip/Postal code...................
Phone ....
Fax ....
Mobile ....
e-mail ....

Name ....
Address ....
....
........................Zip/Postal code....................
Phone ....
Fax ....
Mobile ....
e-mail ....

Name ....
Address ....
....
........................Zip/Postal code....................
Phone ....
Fax ....
Mobile ....
e-mail ....

Name ....
Address ....
....
........................Zip/Postal code....................
Phone ....
Fax ....
Mobile ....
e-mail ....

Name ....
Address ....
....
........................Zip/Postal code....................
Phone ....
Fax ....
Mobile ....
e-mail ....

Name ....
Address ....
....
........................Zip/Postal code....................
Phone ....
Fax ....
Mobile ....
e-mail ....

p

Name ....
Address ....
....
........................Zip/Postal code....................
Phone ....
Fax ....
Mobile ....
e-mail ....

Name ....
Address ....
....
....................Zip/Postal code....................
Phone ....
Fax ....
Mobile ....
e-mail ....

Name ....
Address ....
....
....................Zip/Postal code....................
Phone ....
Fax ....
Mobile ....
e-mail ....

Name ....
Address ....
....
....................Zip/Postal code....................
Phone ....
Fax ....
Mobile ....
e-mail ....

Name ....
Address ....
....
....................Zip/Postal code....................
Phone ....
Fax ....
Mobile ....
e-mail ....

Name ....
Address ....
....
....................Zip/Postal code....................
Phone ....
Fax ....
Mobile ....
e-mail ....

Name ....
Address ....
....
....................Zip/Postal code....................
Phone ....
Fax ....
Mobile ....
e-mail ....

Name ....
Address ....
....
....................Zip/Postal code....................
Phone ....
Fax ....
Mobile ....
e-mail ....

Name ....
Address ....
....
........................Zip/Postal code..................
Phone ....
Fax ....
Mobile ....
e-mail ....

Name ....
Address ....
....
........................Zip/Postal code..................
Phone ....
Fax ....
Mobile ....
e-mail ....

Name ....
Address ....
....
........................Zip/Postal code..................
Phone ....
Fax ....
Mobile ....
e-mail ....

Name ....
Address ....
....
........................Zip/Postal code..................
Phone ....
Fax ....
Mobile ....
e-mail ....

Name ....
Address ....
....
........................Zip/Postal code..................
Phone ....
Fax ....
Mobile ....
e-mail ....

Name ....
Address ....
....
........................Zip/Postal code..................
Phone ....
Fax ....
Mobile ....
e-mail ....

Name ....
Address ....
....
........................Zip/Postal code..................
Phone ....
Fax ....
Mobile ....
e-mail ....

Name ....
Address ....
....
.........................Zip/Postal code.....................
Phone ....
Fax ....
Mobile ....
e-mail ....

Name ....
Address ....
....
.........................Zip/Postal code.....................
Phone ....
Fax ....
Mobile ....
e-mail ....

Name ....
Address ....
....
.........................Zip/Postal code.....................
Phone ....
Fax ....
Mobile ....
e-mail ....

Name ....
Address ....
....
.........................Zip/Postal code.....................
Phone ....
Fax ....
Mobile ....
e-mail ....

Name ....
Address ....
....
.........................Zip/Postal code.....................
Phone ....
Fax ....
Mobile ....
e-mail ....

Name ....
Address ....
....
.........................Zip/Postal code.....................
Phone ....
Fax ....
Mobile ....
e-mail ....

Name ....
Address ....
....
.........................Zip/Postal code.....................
Phone ....
Fax ....
Mobile ....
e-mail ....

q

Name ....
Address ....
....
......................Zip/Postal code.....................
Phone ....
Fax ....
Mobile ....
e-mail ....

Name ....
Address ....
....
......................Zip/Postal code.....................
Phone ....
Fax ....
Mobile ....
e-mail ....

Name ....
Address ....
....
......................Zip/Postal code.....................
Phone ....
Fax ....
Mobile ....
e-mail ....

Name ....
Address ....
....
......................Zip/Postal code.....................
Phone ....
Fax ....
Mobile ....
e-mail ....

Name ....
Address ....
....
......................Zip/Postal code.....................
Phone ....
Fax ....
Mobile ....
e-mail ....

Name ....
Address ....
....
......................Zip/Postal code.....................
Phone ....
Fax ....
Mobile ....
e-mail ....

Name ....
Address ....
....
......................Zip/Postal code.....................
Phone ....
Fax ....
Mobile ....
e-mail ....

Name ....
Address ....
....
........................Zip/Postal code........................
Phone ....
Fax ....
Mobile ....
e-mail ....

Name ....
Address ....
....
........................Zip/Postal code........................
Phone ....
Fax ....
Mobile ....
e-mail ....

Name ....
Address ....
....
........................Zip/Postal code........................
Phone ....
Fax ....
Mobile ....
e-mail ....

Name ....
Address ....
....
........................Zip/Postal code........................
Phone ....
Fax ....
Mobile ....
e-mail ....

Name ....
Address ....
....
........................Zip/Postal code........................
Phone ....
Fax ....
Mobile ....
e-mail ....

Name ....
Address ....
....
........................Zip/Postal code........................
Phone ....
Fax ....
Mobile ....
e-mail ....

Name ....
Address ....
....
........................Zip/Postal code........................
Phone ....
Fax ....
Mobile ....
e-mail ....

Name ....
Address ....
....
.......................Zip/Postal code....................
Phone ....
Fax ....
Mobile ....
e-mail ....

Name ....
Address ....
....
.......................Zip/Postal code....................
Phone ....
Fax ....
Mobile ....
e-mail ....

Name ....
Address ....
....
.......................Zip/Postal code....................
Phone ....
Fax ....
Mobile ....
e-mail ....

Name ....
Address ....
....
.......................Zip/Postal code....................
Phone ....
Fax ....
Mobile ....
e-mail ....

Name ....
Address ....
....
.......................Zip/Postal code....................
Phone ....
Fax ....
Mobile ....
e-mail ....

Name ....
Address ....
....
.......................Zip/Postal code....................
Phone ....
Fax ....
Mobile ....
e-mail ....

Name ....
Address ....
....
.......................Zip/Postal code....................
Phone ....
Fax ....
Mobile ....
e-mail ....

r

Name ....
Address ....
....
.........................Zip/Postal code.................
Phone ....
Fax ....
Mobile ....
e-mail ....

Name ....
Address ....
....
.........................Zip/Postal code.................
Phone ....
Fax ....
Mobile ....
e-mail ....

Name ....
Address ....
....
.........................Zip/Postal code.................
Phone ....
Fax ....
Mobile ....
e-mail ....

Name ....
Address ....
....
.........................Zip/Postal code.................
Phone ....
Fax ....
Mobile ....
e-mail ....

Name ....
Address ....
....
.........................Zip/Postal code.................
Phone ....
Fax ....
Mobile ....
e-mail ....

Name ....
Address ....
....
.........................Zip/Postal code.................
Phone ....
Fax ....
Mobile ....
e-mail ....

Name ....
Address ....
....
.........................Zip/Postal code.................
Phone ....
Fax ....
Mobile ....
e-mail ....

Name ....
Address ....
....
........................Zip/Postal code....................
Phone ....
Fax ....
Mobile ....
e-mail ....

Name ....
Address ....
....
........................Zip/Postal code....................
Phone ....
Fax ....
Mobile ....
e-mail ....

Name ....
Address ....
....
........................Zip/Postal code....................
Phone ....
Fax ....
Mobile ....
e-mail ....

Name ....
Address ....
....
........................Zip/Postal code....................
Phone ....
Fax ....
Mobile ....
e-mail ....

Name ....
Address ....
....
........................Zip/Postal code....................
Phone ....
Fax ....
Mobile ....
e-mail ....

Name ....
Address ....
....
........................Zip/Postal code....................
Phone ....
Fax ....
Mobile ....
e-mail ....

Name ....
Address ....
....
........................Zip/Postal code....................
Phone ....
Fax ....
Mobile ....
e-mail ....

Name ....
Address ....
....
.........................Zip/Postal code.....................
Phone ....
Fax ....
Mobile ....
e-mail ....

Name ....
Address ....
....
.........................Zip/Postal code.....................
Phone ....
Fax ....
Mobile ....
e-mail ....

Name ....
Address ....
....
.........................Zip/Postal code.....................
Phone ....
Fax ....
Mobile ....
e-mail ....

Name ....
Address ....
....
.........................Zip/Postal code.....................
Phone ....
Fax ....
Mobile ....
e-mail ....

Name ....
Address ....
....
.........................Zip/Postal code.....................
Phone ....
Fax ....
Mobile ....
e-mail ....

Name ....
Address ....
....
.........................Zip/Postal code.....................
Phone ....
Fax ....
Mobile ....
e-mail ....

S

Name ....
Address ....
....
.........................Zip/Postal code.....................
Phone ....
Fax ....
Mobile ....
e-mail ....

Name ....
Address ....
....
...................Zip/Postal code..................
Phone ....
Fax ....
Mobile ....
e-mail ....

Name ....
Address ....
....
...................Zip/Postal code..................
Phone ....
Fax ....
Mobile ....
e-mail ....

Name ....
Address ....
....
...................Zip/Postal code..................
Phone ....
Fax ....
Mobile ....
e-mail ....

Name ....
Address ....
....
...................Zip/Postal code..................
Phone ....
Fax ....
Mobile ....
e-mail ....

Name ....
Address ....
....
...................Zip/Postal code..................
Phone ....
Fax ....
Mobile ....
e-mail ....

Name ....
Address ....
....
...................Zip/Postal code..................
Phone ....
Fax ....
Mobile ....
e-mail ....

Name ....
Address ....
....
...................Zip/Postal code..................
Phone ....
Fax ....
Mobile ....
e-mail ....

S

Name ....
Address ....
....
.........................Zip/Postal code....................
Phone ....
Fax ....
Mobile ....
e-mail ....

Name ....
Address ....
....
.........................Zip/Postal code....................
Phone ....
Fax ....
Mobile ....
e-mail ....

Name ....
Address ....
....
.........................Zip/Postal code....................
Phone ....
Fax ....
Mobile ....
e-mail ....

Name ....
Address ....
....
.........................Zip/Postal code....................
Phone ....
Fax ....
Mobile ....
e-mail ....

Name ....
Address ....
....
.........................Zip/Postal code....................
Phone ....
Fax ....
Mobile ....
e-mail ....

S

Name ....
Address ....
....
.........................Zip/Postal code....................
Phone ....
Fax ....
Mobile ....
e-mail ....

Name ....
Address ....
....
.........................Zip/Postal code...................
Phone ....
Fax ....
Mobile ....
e-mail ....

Name ....
Address ....
....
.........................Zip/Postal code ....
Phone ....
Fax ....
Mobile ....
e-mail ....

Name ....
Address ....
....
.........................Zip/Postal code...................
Phone ....
Fax ....
Mobile ....
e-mail ....

Name ....
Address ....
....
.........................Zip/Postal code...................
Phone ....
Fax ....
Mobile ....
e-mail ....

Name ....
Address ....
....
.........................Zip/Postal code...................
Phone ....
Fax ....
Mobile ....
e-mail ....

Name ....
Address ....
....
.........................Zip/Postal code...................
Phone ....
Fax ....
Mobile ....
e-mail ....

Name ....
Address ....
....
.........................Zip/Postal code...................
Phone ....
Fax ....
Mobile ....
e-mail ....

Name ....
Address ....
....
.........................Zip/Postal code...................
Phone ....
Fax ....
Mobile ....
e-mail ....

Name ....
Address ....
....
.........................Zip/Postal code...................
Phone ....
Fax ....
Mobile ....
e-mail ....

Name ....
Address ....
....
.........................Zip/Postal code...................
Phone ....
Fax ....
Mobile ....
e-mail ....

Name ....
Address ....
....
.........................Zip/Postal code...................
Phone ....
Fax ....
Mobile ....
e-mail ....

Name ....
Address ....
....
.........................Zip/Postal code...................
Phone ....
Fax ....
Mobile ....
e-mail ....

Name ....
Address ....
....
.........................Zip/Postal code...................
Phone ....
Fax ....
Mobile ....
e-mail ....

Name ....
Address ....
....
.........................Zip/Postal code...................
Phone ....
Fax ....
Mobile ....
e-mail ....

Name ....
Address ....
....
........................Zip/Postal code...................
Phone ....
Fax ....
Mobile ....
e-mail ....

Name ....
Address ....
....
........................Zip/Postal code...................
Phone ....
Fax ....
Mobile ....
e-mail ....

Name ....
Address ....
....
........................Zip/Postal code...................
Phone ....
Fax ....
Mobile ....
e-mail ....

Name ....
Address ....
....
........................Zip/Postal code...................
Phone ....
Fax ....
Mobile ....
e-mail ....

Name ....
Address ....
....
........................Zip/Postal code...................
Phone ....
Fax ....
Mobile ....
e-mail ....

Name ....
Address ....
....
........................Zip/Postal code...................
Phone ....
Fax ....
Mobile ....
e-mail ....

Name ....
Address ....
....
.........................Zip/Postal code.....................
Phone ....
Fax ....
Mobile ....
e-mail ....

Name ....
Address ....
....
.........................Zip/Postal code.....................
Phone ....
Fax ....
Mobile ....
e-mail ....

Name ....
Address ....
....
.........................Zip/Postal code.....................
Phone ....
Fax ....
Mobile ....
e-mail ....

Name ....
Address ....
....
.........................Zip/Postal code.....................
Phone ....
Fax ....
Mobile ....
e-mail ....

Name ....
Address ....
....
.........................Zip/Postal code.....................
Phone ....
Fax ....
Mobile ....
e-mail ....

Name ....
Address ....
....
.........................Zip/Postal code.....................
Phone ....
Fax ....
Mobile ....
e-mail ....

Name ....
Address ....
....
.........................Zip/Postal code.....................
Phone ....
Fax ....
Mobile ....
e-mail ....

t

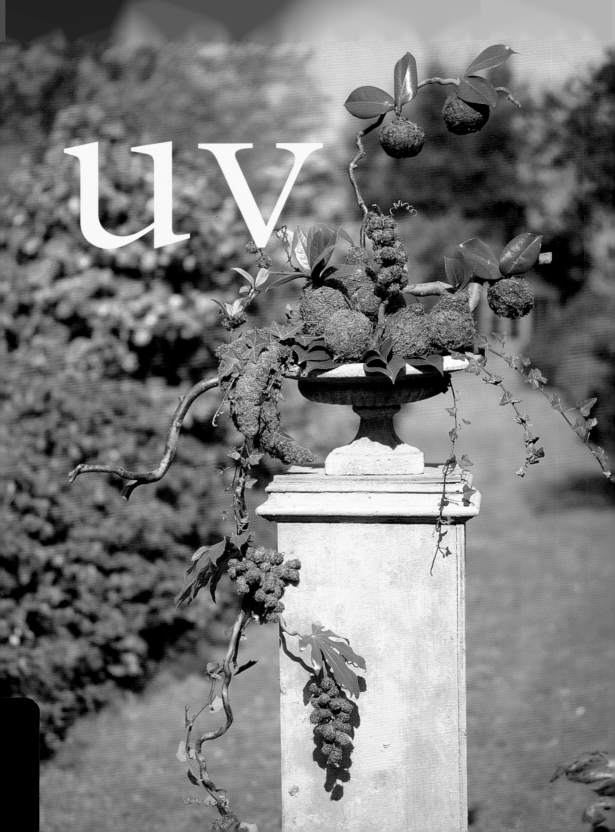

Name ....
Address ....
....
....................Zip/Postal code................
Phone ....
Fax ....
Mobile ....
e-mail ....

Name ....
Address ....
....
....................Zip/Postal code................
Phone ....
Fax ....
Mobile ....
e-mail ....

Name ....
Address ....
....
....................Zip/Postal code................
Phone ....
Fax ....
Mobile ....
e-mail ....

Name ....
Address ....
....
....................Zip/Postal code................
Phone ....
Fax ....
Mobile ....
e-mail ....

Name ....
Address ....
....
....................Zip/Postal code................
Phone ....
Fax ....
Mobile ....
e-mail ....

Name ....
Address ....
....
....................Zip/Postal code................
Phone ....
Fax ....
Mobile ....
e-mail ....

Name ....
Address ....
....
....................Zip/Postal code................
Phone ....
Fax ....
Mobile ....
e-mail ....

W

Name ....
Address ....
....
.........................Zip/Postal code.......................
Phone ....
Fax ....
Mobile ....
e-mail ....

Name ....
Address ....
....
.........................Zip/Postal code.......................
Phone ....
Fax ....
Mobile ....
e-mail ....

Name ....
Address ....
....
.........................Zip/Postal code.......................
Phone ....
Fax ....
Mobile ....
e-mail ....

Name ....
Address ....
....
.........................Zip/Postal code.......................
Phone ....
Fax ....
Mobile ....
e-mail ....

Name ....
Address ....
....
.........................Zip/Postal code.......................
Phone ....
Fax ....
Mobile ....
e-mail ....

Name ....
Address ....
....
.........................Zip/Postal code.......................
Phone ....
Fax ....
Mobile ....
e-mail ....

Name ....
Address ....
....
.........................Zip/Postal code.......................
Phone ....
Fax ....
Mobile ....
e-mail ....

Name ....
Address ....
....
.............................Zip/Postal code....................
Phone ....
Fax ....
Mobile ....
e-mail ....

Name ....
Address ....
....
.............................Zip/Postal code....................
Phone ....
Fax ....
Mobile ....
e-mail ....

Name ....
Address ....
....
.............................Zip/Postal code....................
Phone ....
Fax ....
Mobile ....
e-mail ....

Name ....
Address ....
....
.............................Zip/Postal code....................
Phone ....
Fax ....
Mobile ....
e-mail ....

Name ....
Address ....
....
.............................Zip/Postal code....................
Phone ....
Fax ....
Mobile ....
e-mail ....

Name ....
Address ....
....
.............................Zip/Postal code....................
Phone ....
Fax ....
Mobile ....
e-mail ....

W

Name ....
Address ....
....
......................Zip/Postal code...................
Phone ....
Fax ....
Mobile ....
e-mail ....

Name ....
Address ....
....
......................Zip/Postal code ....
Phone ....
Fax ....
Mobile ....
e-mail ....

Name ....
Address ....
....
......................Zip/Postal code...................
Phone ....
Fax ....
Mobile ....
e-mail ....

Name ....
Address ....
....
......................Zip/Postal code..................
Phone ....
Fax ....
Mobile ....
e-mail ....

Name ....
Address ....
....
......................Zip/Postal code...................
Phone ....
Fax ....
Mobile ....
e-mail ....

Name ....
Address ....
....
......................Zip/Postal code..................
Phone ....
Fax ....
Mobile ....
e-mail ....

Name ....
Address ....
....
......................Zip/Postal code...................
Phone ....
Fax ....
Mobile ....
e-mail ....

Name ....
Address ....
....
.....................Zip/Postal code...................
Phone ....
Fax ....
Mobile ....
e-mail ....

Name ....
Address ....
....
.....................Zip/Postal code...................
Phone ....
Fax ....
Mobile ....
e-mail ....

Name ....
Address ....
....
.....................Zip/Postal code...................
Phone ....
Fax ....
Mobile ....
e-mail ....

Name ....
Address ....
....
.....................Zip/Postal code...................
Phone ....
Fax ....
Mobile ....
e-mail ....

Name ....
Address ....
....
.....................Zip/Postal code...................
Phone ....
Fax ....
Mobile ....
e-mail ....

Name ....
Address ....
....
.....................Zip/Postal code...................
Phone ....
Fax ....
Mobile ....
e-mail ....

Name ....
Address ....
....
.....................Zip/Postal code...................
Phone ....
Fax ....
Mobile ....
e-mail ....

xy

Name ....
Address ....
....
..........................Zip/Postal code.....................
Phone ....
Fax ....
Mobile ....
e-mail ....

Name ....
Address ....
....
..........................Zip/Postal code.....................
Phone ....
Fax ....
Mobile ....
e-mail ....

Name ....
Address ....
....
..........................Zip/Postal code.....................
Phone ....
Fax ....
Mobile ....
e-mail ....

Name ....
Address ....
....
..........................Zip/Postal code.....................
Phone ....
Fax ....
Mobile ....
e-mail ....

Name ....
Address ....
....
..........................Zip/Postal code.....................
Phone ....
Fax ....
Mobile ....
e-mail ....

Name ....
Address ....
....
..........................Zip/Postal code.....................
Phone ....
Fax ....
Mobile ....
e-mail ....

Name ....
Address ....
....
..........................Zip/Postal code.....................
Phone ....
Fax ....
Mobile ....
e-mail ....

birthdays,
anniversaries
and events

January

	1	2	3
4	5	6	7
8	9	10	11
12	13	14	15

January

16	17	18	19
20	21	22	23
24	25	26	27
28	29	30	31

February

		1	2
3	4	5	6
7	8	9	10
11	12	13	14

February

15	16	17	18
19	20	21	22
23	24	25	26
27	28 / 29		

March

	1	2	3
4	5	6	7
8	9	10	11
12	13	14	15

March

16	17	18	19
20	21	22	23
24	25	26	27
28	29	30	31

April

	1	2	3
4	5	6	7
8	9	10	11
12	13	14	15

April

16	17	18	19
20	21	22	23
24	25	26	27
28	29	30	

May

1	2	3	4
5	6	7	8
9	10	11	12
13	14	15	16

May

17	18	19	20
21	22	23	24
25	26	27	28
29	30	31	

June

	1	2	3
4	5	6	7
8	9	10	11
12	13	14	15

June

16	17	18	19
20	21	22	23
24	25	26	27
28	29	30	

July

	1	2	3
4	5	6	7
8	9	10	11
12	13	14	15

July

16	17	18	19
20	21	22	23
24	25	26	27
28	29	30	31

August

1	2	3	4
5	6	7	8
9	10	11	12
13	14	15	16

August

17	18	19	20
21	22	23	24
25	26	27	28
29	30	31	

September

	1	2	3
4	5	6	7
8	9	10	11
12	13	14	15

September

16	17	18	19
20	21	22	23
24	25	26	27
28	29	30	

October

	1	2	3
4	5	6	7
8	9	10	11
12	13	14	15

and events

October

16	17	18	19
20	21	22	23
24	25	26	27
28	29	30	31

November

	1	2	3
4	5	6	7
8	9	10	11
12	13	14	15

November

16	17	18	19
20	21	22	23
24	25	26	27
28	29	30	

December

1	2	3
4	5	6	7
8	9	10	11
12	13	14	15

December

16	17	18	19
20	21	22	23
24	25	26	27
28	29	30	31

gifts &
ideas list

Name	Occasion	Date
....	....	....
....	....	....
....	....	....
....	....	....
....	....	....
....	....	....
....	....	....
....	....	....
....	....	....
....	....	....
....	....	....
....	....	....
....	....	....
....	....	....
....	....	....
....	....	....
....	....	....
....	....	....
....	....	....
....	....	....
....	....	....
....	....	....

Notes

....
....
....
....
....
....

Name	Occasion	Date
....	....	....
....	....	....
....	....	....
....	....	....
....	....	....
....	....	....
....	....	....
....	....	....
....	....	....
....	....	....
....	....	....
....	....	....
....	....	....
....	....	....
....	....	....
....	....	....
....	....	....
....	....	....
....	....	....
....	....	....
....	....	....
....	....	....
....	....	....

Notes

....
....
....
....
....
....

Name	Occasion	Date
....	....	....
....	....	....
....	....	....
....	....	....
....	....	....
....	....	....
....	....	....
....	....	....
....	....	....
....	....	....
....	....	....
....	....	....
....	....	....
....	....	....
....	....	....
....	....	....
....	....	....
....	....	....
....	....	....
....	....	....
....	....	....
....	....	....
....	....	....

Notes

....
....
....
....
....
....

Name	Occasion	Date

Notes

Name	Occasion	Date

Notes

Name	Occasion	Date

Notes

Name	Occasion	Date
....	....	....
....	....	....
....	....	....
....	....	....
....	....	....
....	....	....
....	....	....
....	....	....
....	....	....
....	....	....
....	....	....
....	....	....
....	....	....
....	....	....
....	....	....
....	....	....
....	....	....
....	....	....
....	....	....
....	....	....
....	....	....
....	....	....
....	....	....
....	....	....

Notes

....
....
....
....
....
....

Name	Occasion	Date
....	....	....
....	....	....
....	....	....
....	....	....
....	....	....
....	....	....
....	....	....
....	....	....
....	....	....
....	....	....
....	....	....
....	....	....
....	....	....
....	....	....
....	....	....
....	....	....
....	....	....
....	....	....
....	....	....
....	....	....
....	....	....

Notes

....

....

....

....

....

....

Name	Occasion	Date
....	....	....
....	....	....
....	....	....
....	....	....
....	....	....
....	....	....
....	....	....
....	....	....
....	....	....
....	....	....
....	....	....
....	....	....
....	....	....
....	....	....
....	....	....
....	....	....
....	....	....
....	....	....
....	....	....
....	....	....
....	....	....
....	....	....

Notes

....

....

....

....

....

....

Name	Occasion	Date
....	....	....
....	....	....
....	....	....
....	....	....
....	....	....
....	....	....
....	....	....
....	....	....
....	....	....
....	....	....
....	....	....
....	....	....
....	....	....
....	....	....
....	....	....
....	....	....
....	....	....
....	....	....
....	....	....
....	....	....
....	....	....
....	....	....
....	....	....
....	....	....

Notes

....
....
....
....
....
....

Name	Occasion	Date
....	....	....
....	....	....
....	....	....
....	....	....
....	....	....
....	....	....
....	....	....
....	....	....
....	....	....
....	....	....
....	....	....
....	....	....
....	....	....
....	....	....
....	....	....
....	....	....
....	....	....
....	....	....
....	....	....
....	....	....
....	....	....
....	....	....

Notes

....
....
....
....
....

Name	Occasion	Date

Notes

....
....
....
....
....
....

christma
card lis

Name	....	Year ....
Name	....	Year ....
Name	....	Year ....
Name	....	Year ....
Name	....	Year ....
Name	....	Year ....
Name	....	Year ....
Name	....	Year ....
Name	....	Year ....
Name	....	Year ....
Name	....	Year ....
Name	....	Year ....
Name	....	Year ....
Name	....	Year ....
Name	....	Year ....
Name	....	Year ....
Name	....	Year ....
Name	....	Year ....
Name	....	Year ....
Name	....	Year ....
Name	....	Year ....
Name	....	Year ....
Name	....	Year ....
Name	....	Year ....
Name	....	Year ....

Notes

....

....

....

....

....

....

Name		Year	
Name	....	Year	....
Name	....	Year	....
Name	....	Year	....
Name	....	Year	....
Name	....	Year	....
Name	....	Year	....
Name	....	Year	....
Name	....	Year	....
Name	....	Year	....
Name	....	Year	....
Name	....	Year	....
Name	....	Year	....
Name	....	Year	....
Name	....	Year	....
Name	....	Year	....
Name	....	Year	....
Name	....	Year	....
Name	....	Year	....
Name	....	Year	....
Name	....	Year	....
Name	....	Year	....
Name	....	Year	....
Name	....	Year	....
Name	....	Year	....
Name	....	Year	....
Name	....	Year	....
Name	....	Year	....

Notes

....
....
....
....
....
....

Name	....	Year	....
Name	....	Year	....
Name	....	Year	....
Name	....	Year	....
Name	....	Year	....
Name	....	Year	....
Name	....	Year	....
Name	....	Year	....
Name	....	Year	....
Name	....	Year	....
Name	....	Year	....
Name	....	Year	....
Name	....	Year	....
Name	....	Year	....
Name	....	Year	....
Name	....	Year	....
Name	....	Year	....
Name	....	Year	....
Name	....	Year	....
Name	....	Year	....
Name	....	Year	....
Name	....	Year	....
Name	....	Year	....
Name	....	Year	....
Name	....	Year	....

Notes

....

....

....

....

....

....